THE BIG BOOK OF SCIENCE JOKES

LEARN WHILE YOU LAUGH

TIM KESSLER

DEDICATION

To my wife Vella, who laughs at all my jokes even when I know darn well some of them are not that funny.

To my daughter Angel, who tells me how proud she is of me each day.

To my son Pierce, who makes life so much fun to live.

CONTENTS

INTRODUCTION

Science is probably one of the most fascinating things to study. But the study or science is really wide, with all its branches. Add in the thousands of theories, hypothesis and formulas and it would bring any grown person to tears.

I have always had a fascination with science and even to this very day still keep up with the latest news in all the various fields. And I have found that the best way to learn about science is by making it a fun activity.

What better way to make something fun than to joke about it? This book contains hundreds of jokes on the various fields of science. It is the perfect way to expand your knowledge as well as have a good laugh.

I have found that sometimes when telling a science joke, the person hearing the joke either does not get it or wants to know something about the joke I just told. And arming yourself with the backup knowledge to explain the joke will be invaluable.

This joke book is meant for a lot of different people:

- It is meant for the parent who wants their kids to know more about science.

- It is meant for the teenager who wants to show off his intelligence by spouting off intelligent humor.

- It is meant for the professor who wants to inject some humor in his lectures.

- It is meant for anyone who just wants a good laugh.

It is my hope that you enjoy all the jokes in this book and at the same time learn something new today.

The author

1 PALAEONTOLOGY
"The study of life on Earth from a very long time ago."

Q: What do you call a dinosaur with no eyes?
A: Doyouthinkysaraus

Q: What do you call a sleeping dinosaur?
A: A dino-snore!

Q: How do you know if there is a dinosaur in your refrigerator?
A: The door won't shut!

Q: What dinosaur would Harry Potter be?
A: The Dinosorcerer

Q: How can you best raise a baby dinosaur?
A: With a crane!

Q: What did the dinosaur put on her steak?
A: Dinosauce

Q: Why was the Stegosaurus such a good volleyball player?
A: Because he could really spike the ball!

Q: What came after the dinosaur?
A: Its tail!

Q: What does a Triceratops sit on?
A: Its tricera-bottom.

Q: What do dinosaurs use on the floors of their kitchens?
A: Rep-tiles

Q: What is the best thing to do if you see a Tyrannosaurus Rex?
A: Pray that it doesn't see you.

Q: What's the nickname for someone who put their right hand in the mouth of a T-Rex?
A: Lefty

Q: What game does the Brontosaurus like to play with humans?
A: Squash

Q: Why did the dinosaur cross the road?
A: To eat the chickens on the other side.

Q: What do you call a Paleontologist who sleeps all the time?
A: Lazy bones

Q: What do you get when a dinosaur scores a touchdown?
A: A dino-score

Q: What did the dinosaur use to build his house?
A: A dino-saw

Q: What do you call two dinosaurs that have been in an accident?
A: Tyrannosaurus wrecks

Q: Why do museums have old dinosaur bones?
A: Because they can't afford new ones!

Q: Why did the tyrannosaur cross the road?
A: Because chickens hadn't evolved yet.

Q: What's the best way to talk to a velociraptor?
A: Long distance!

Q: How do you ask a tyrannosaur out to lunch?
A: "Tea, Rex?"

Dad: Why are you crying?
Son: Because I wanted to get a dinosaur for my baby sister.
Dad: That's no reason to cry.
Son: Yes, it is. No one would trade me!

Q: How do you know there's a seismosaurus under your bed?
A: Because your nose is two inches from the ceiling!

Q: What's worse than a giraffe with a sore throat?
A: A tyrannosaur with a giraffe in its throat!

Q: Why can't you hear a pterosaur using the bathroom?
A: Because the "p" is silent!

Q: How can you tell there's an allosaurus in your bed?
A: By the bright red "A" on its pajamas.

Person 1: I keep seeing pteranodons with orange polka dots.
Person 2: Have you seen an eye doctor yet?
Person 1: No, just pteranodons with orange polka dots!

Q: What did dinosaurs use to make their hot dogs?
A: Jurassic pork!

2 CHEMISTRY

"The study of matter and the chemical reactions between substances."

Q: What do you do with a dead chemist?
A: Barium.

Q: Why are chemists perfect for solving problems?
A: Because they have all the solutions.

Q: Where do chemists wash their dirty dishes?
A: In the zinc.

Q: Why do chemists prefer nitrates?
A: Because they're cheaper than day rates.

Atom: I'd like to report a missing electron.
Policeman: Are you sure?
Atom: Yes, I'm positive!

Q: What's the first thing you should learn in chemistry?
A: Never lick the spoon.

Q: Why did hydrogen marry carbon?
A: Because they bonded so well.

A neutron walks into a bar and asks, "How much for a drink?"
The bartender replies, "For you, no charge."

Q: What kind of ghosts haunt chemistry labs?
A: What kind of ghosts haunt chemistry labs? Methylated Spirits.

Q: Did you hear the joke about Sodium hypobromite?
A: NaBrO

I don't trust Atoms.
They make up everything!

Q: What do you do if your chemistry teacher is sick?
A: If you can't Helium or Curium, you Barium.

I was going to tell you a chemistry joke, but all the good ones Argon.

There's a night club just for chemistry students…. I hear they're really good at dropping the base

I was reading a book on Helium.
I couldn't put it down.

Q: Anyone know any jokes about sodium?
A: Na

2 men walk into a bar.
#1 says: I'll have a glass of H2O pls. After drinking it all, he was refreshed.
#2 says: I'll have a glass of H2O too. He drank his glass & died. Hmmmm. Do you know why?

My science teacher took a drink,
Now she shall drink no more,
For what she thought was H2O,
Was H2SO4.

Q: Did you hear oxygen went on a date with potassium?
A: It went OK.

If the Silver Surfer and Iron Man team up, they'd be alloys.

Organic chemistry is difficult.
Those who study it have alkynes of trouble.

Q: What do chemists call a benzene ring with iron atoms replacing the carbon atoms?
A: A ferrous wheel.

Helium walks into a bar and asks for a drink.
The bartender says, "Sorry, we don't serve noble gases here."
Helium doesn't react.

Q: What do you call a joke that is based on cobalt, radon, and yttrium?
A: CoRnY.

Q: What does a teary-eyed, joyful Santa say about chemistry?
A: HOH, HOH, HOH!

I would make a chemistry pun but it'd be easily miscible

Q: Want to hear a Potassium joke?
A: K.

Q: Did you hear about the chemist who was reading a book about helium?
A: He couldn't put it down!

Q: If H2O is the formula for water, what is the formula for ice?
A: H2O cubed

Q: What did their parents say when they heard that Oxygen and Magnesium were going to get married?
A: OMg

3 BIOLOGY
"The study of life and living organisms."

Q: What do you call the leader of a biology gang?
A: The nucleus.

Genetics explains why you look like your father, and if you don't, why you probably should.

Q: Why are frogs so happy?
A: Because they can eat whatever bugs them!

Q: How do you spot a bald eagle?
A: Look for a bird with all its feathers combed over to one side.

The pistil of a flower is its last line of defense against insects.

I've never been a good swimmer, my DNA almost drowned in its gene pool.

Mushrooms look like umbrellas because they grow in damp places.

Q: Why do tigers have stripes?
A: So they don't get spotted.

Q: Why did the germ cross the microscope?
A: To get to the other slide!

Q: Why does the spinal cord belong in the brass section of an orchestra?
A: Because it has dorsal and ventral horns.

Q: Did you hear about the famous microbiologist who visited 30 different countries and spoke 6 languages?
A: He was a man of many cultures.

Q: What's the difference between a dog and a marine biologist?
A: One wags a tail and the other tags a whale.

Q: What did the dog say to his owner?
A: My favorite frequency is 50,000 hertz but you've probably never heard of that.

Q: What did the stamen say to the pistil?
A: I like your style!

Q: What did the microbiology student get for being late to class?
A: A tardigrade.

Q: How much room do fungi need to grow?
A: As mushroom as possible.

Q: Do you know the name Pavlov?
A: It rings a bell.

Two blood cells met and fell in love.
Alas it was all in vein.

We really need to stop talking about mitosis. It's such a divisive issue.

Q: Why did the Biologist not water all the plants?
A: Because he couldn't find the thyme.

One plant says to another: "Are you hungry?"
The other replies: "Yes, I could use a light snack."

Q: What does a Biologist wear on a first date?
A: Designer genes.

Q: When a plant is sad, what do the other plants do?
A: Photosympathise

Q: What type of flower does everyone own?
A: Two-lips

Q: What is blood's message to the world?
A: B positive

Q: What did the brother cell say to the sister cell when she stepped on his foot?
A: Mitosis

Q: Why can't a plant be on the darkside of the Force?
A: Because it can't make food without the light!

Q: Why was the scuba diver failing Biology?
A: Because he was below "C" level.

Q: How many biologists does it take to change a light bulb?
A: Four. One to change it and three to write the environmental-impact statement.

4 PHYSICS
"The study of matter and its motion through space and time, along with related concepts such as energy and force."

Q: Where does bad light go?
A: To a prism.

Q: How did Einstein begin his stories?
A: Once upon a space-time...

Q: What's a nuclear physicist's favorite meal?
A: Fission chips.

A quantum physicist walks into a bar......maybe.

Q: Who solves mysteries involving electricity?
A: Sherlock Ohms

Q: What's the matter?
A: Solid, liquid, gas

Einstein developed a theory about space.
It was about time too.

You Matter!
Unless you multiply yourself by the speed of light...... then you energy

A photon checks into a hotel and is asked if he needs any help with his luggage. He says, "No, I'm travelling light."

Q: Did you hear about the man who got cooled to absolute zero?
A: He's 0K now.

Q: Why is quantum mechanics is the original "original hipster"?
A: It described the universe before it was cool.

Q: What did one quantum physicist say when he wanted to fight another quantum physicist?
A: Let me Atom

Q: What did one uranium-238 nucleus say to the other?
A: "Gotta split!"

Q: Why is electricity an ideal citizen?
A: Because it conducts itself so well.

Q: Which books are the hardest to force yourself to read through?
A: Friction books.

Q: What happens when electrons lose their energy?
A: They get Bohr'ed.

Unknown Fact: You can be cooled to -273.15C and be 0K.

What do we want? Time travel!
When do we want it? Irrelevant!

I have a new theory on inertia, but it doesn't seem to be gaining momentum.

Q: What does a subatomic duck say?
A: Quark!

Q: Are you going to finish that atom?
A: You want to split it?

Atom 1: "I think I've lost an electron."
Atom 2: "Are you sure?"
Atom 1: "I'm positive."

Q: How many theoretical physicists specializing in general relativity does it take to change a light bulb?
A: Two. One to hold the bulb and one to rotate the universe.

Q: Why can't you trust an atom?
A: They make up everything.

When a third grader was asked to cite Newton's first law, she said, "Bodies in motion remain in motion, and bodies at rest stay in bed unless their mothers call them to get up."

When a third-grade student was asked to define the term "vacuum" in class, she answered, "A vacuum is an empty region of space where the Pope lives."

Q: What did one quantum physicist say when he wanted to fight another quantum physicist?
A: Let me atom.

Q: What did Donald Duck say in his graduate physics class?
A: Quark, quark, quark!

According to Einstein's Theory of Relatives, the probability of in-laws visiting you is directly proportional to how much you feel like being left alone.

Q: What did the male magnet say to the female magnet?
A: From your backside, I thought you were repulsive. However, after seeing you from the front, I find you rather attractive.

5 ASTRONOMY
"The study of the universe."

Q: Why couldn't the astronaut book a room on the moon?
A: Because it was full.

Q: How do astronauts serve dinner?
A: On flying saucers.

When people run round in circles, we say they're crazy.
When planets do it, we say they're orbiting.

Q: When do astronauts eat their lunch?
A: At launch time.

Q: Why does NASA believe there might be life on Mars?
A: The CD player was stolen from their Mars rover.

Star light, star bright
First star I see tonight
I wish I may, I wish I might
Oh wait, it's just a satellite

Q: How many astronomers does it take to change a light bulb?
A: None, astronomers aren't scared of the dark.

Q: How far can you see on a clear day?
A: 150 million kilometres, from here to the Sun.

While living on Earth might be a little expensive, at least you get a free trip around the Sun every year.

Q: What do you think of that new restaurant on the moon?
A: The food's great but it has no atmosphere.

If you're thinking about telescopes as a hobby, you should look into it.

Q: How do astronomers organize a party?
A: They planet.

It is reported that Copernicus' parents said the following to him at the age of twelve: "Copernicus, young man, when are you going to come to terms with the fact that the world does not revolve around you.

Q: How does the moon cut his hair?
A: Eclipse it!

Q: How do you know when the moon is going broke?
A: When it's down to its last quarter.

Q: What did Neil Armstrong say when no one laughed at his moon jokes?
A: "I guess you had to be there."

Q: Which is closer, Florida or the moon?
A: The moon. You can't see Florida from here.

Q: Why is a moon rock tastier than an Earth rock?
A: It's a little meteor.

Q: Why didn't the sun go to college?
A: Because it already had a million degrees!

Q: What do planets like to read?
A: Comet books!

Q: Did you hear the one about the astronaut who stepped in gum?
A: He got stuck in Orbit.

Q: What does Earth say to tease the other planets?
A: "You guys have no life."

Q: Where do astronauts like to party?
A: The space bar.

Q: What do visitors to the International Space Station have to do before boarding?
A: Pay the parking meteor.

Q: What did the astronomer's friends do after he didn't win the Nobel Prize?
A: They gave him a constellation prize.

Q: What did Neil Armstrong do after he stepped on Buzz Aldrin's toe?
A: He Apollo-gized.

Q: What's a light-year?
A: The same as a regular year, but with less calories.

Q: What kind of stars wear sunglasses?
A: Movie stars

Q: Why did the star get arrested?
A: Because it was a shooting star!

Q: How do you get a baby astronaut to sleep?
A: You rocket!

6 METEOROLOGY
"The study of the atmosphere that focuses on weather processes and forecasting."

Q: Who does everyone listen to but never believe?
A: The weatherman.

Q: What's the weather report for Mexico?
A: Chili today and hot tamale.

It only rains twice a year in England: July through March and April through June.

Q: What's the opposite of a cold front?
A: A warm back.

Q: Hey what's the weather like out there?
A: I don't know yet, I'll tell you when it clears.

Q: What's a tornado's favorite game?
A: Twister!

Q: Where do meteorologists stop for a drink?
A: The closest isobar.

Q: How did the hurricane see?
A: With its eye.

Q: How did you find the weather at camp?
A: It was easy. I just went outside, and there it was!

Q: If an orchestra plays in a thunderstorm, who is most likely to get hit by lightning?
A: The conductor.

Q: Why did the weather forecaster move to another country?
A: Because the weather didn't agree with him.

Q: What do clouds do when they become rich?
A: They make it rain!

Q: What did the snowman and his wife put over their baby's crib?
A: A snowmobile!

Q: What did the evaporating raindrop say?
A: I'm going to pieces.

Q: What do you call a wet bear?
A: A drizzly bear

Q: What goes up when the rain comes down?
A: An Umbrella.

Q: Why did the man use ketchup in the rain?
A: Because it was raining cats and hot dogs

Q: What did one raindrop say to the other?
A: Two's company, three's a cloud

Q: What's the difference between a horse and the weather?
A: One is reined up and the other rains down.

Q: When does it rain money?
A: When there is "change" in the weather.

Q: What did the thermometer say to the other thermometer?
A: You make my temperature rise.

Q: Whatever happened to the cow that was lifted into the air by the tornado?
A: Udder disaster!

Q: What did the lightning bolt say to the other lightning bolt?
A: You're shocking!

Q: What type of cloud is so lazy, because it will never get up?
A: Fog!

Q: What does a cloud wear under his raincoat?
A: Thunderwear!

According to a news story, if global warming continues, in 20 years the only chance we'll have to see a polar bear is in a zoo. So in other words, nothing is going to change.

Q: What happens when fog lifts in California?
A: UCLA!

Q: What did one raindrop say to the other raindrop?
A: My plop is bigger than your plop.

Q: What's the difference between weather and climate?
A: You can't weather a tree, but you can climate.

Q: What happens when it rains cats and dogs?
A: You have to be careful not to step in a poodle.

7 GEOGRAPHY & GEOLOGY
"The study of the Earth, of places and the relationships between people and their environments."

Q: So are you going to visit Egypt?
A: Hmm, I sphinx so.

Q: What did the sea say to the shore?
A: Nothing, it just waved.

Q: What should we do with crude oil?
A: Teach it some manners of course!

Q: What's the fastest country in the world?
A: Russia

Never lend a geologist money. They think a short-term loan is a million years.

If you look carefully at some rocks, you can see the fossil footprints of fishes.

A volcano is a mountain with hiccups.

Watson: Holmes, what kind of rock is this?
Sherlock Holmes: Why that's sedimentary, my dear Watson.

Q: Why would a geologist take his girlfriend to a quarry?
A: Because he wants to get a little boulder.

Q: What did the rock say to the geologist?
A: Don't take me for granite.

Igneous is bliss.

Q: What did the volcano say to his wife?
A: I lava you

On tectonic plate bumped into another.
"Sorry, it was my fault"

Q: Wanna hear the mountain joke?
A: Nah, you won't get over it

Q: Why do Geologists go to concerts?
A: To get their "Rock" On.

Q: Where do geologists like to relax?
A: In a rocking chair

My rocks are gneiss, don't take them for granite.

Some of these jokes just fluorite over my head

Q: What did the beach say when the tide came in?
A: Long time no sea.

8 MATHEMATICS
"The study of numbers, shapes and patterns."

Q: Why did the chicken cross the mobius strip?
A: To get to the same side!

Q: What did the 30-degree angle say to the 90-degree angle?
A: "You think you're always right!"

Q: Why can't you argue with Pi?
A: It's irrational.

There are 10 kinds of people: Those who understand binary and those who don't.

Q: What do you call a number that can't sit still?
A: A roamin' numeral

Q: Why did the two 4's skip lunch?
A: They already 8

Q: What did one maths book say to the other?
A: "Don't bother me, I've got my own problems."

When she told me I was average, she was just being mean.

9 LET'S LEARN PALEONTOLOGY

Paleontology is the study of life that existed on Earth for a very long time ago and which are now extinct. Remember the movie Jurassic Park? Well, Paleontologists don't just study dinosaurs. They also study other animals, plants, fungi and even single celled organisms. They do this by digging around for fossil, from remote mountains to deep valleys.

Fossils are the bones of animals that have solidified over the ages and turned into rock. For softer, boneless animals, plants and one cell organisms, their fossils are impressions left behind on rocks after they have died. Paleontologists very carefully dig out and clean these fossils and try to piece then together like a jigsaw puzzle to form a complete animal or plant. You can find lots of these bones and fossils in all the major museums around the world.

The Earth is said to be 4.5 million years old and life is thought to have appeared around 3.5 billion years ago. To help visualize such a large time scale, paleontologists divide the time into eras, from the Archean Era to the current Holocene Era.

Dinosaurs are a class of reptiles that are believed to have existed between the Triassic Era, through the Jurassic Era and went extinct at the end of the Cretaceous Era. They dominated the Earth for more than 140 million years. We know from movies about the huge scary ones, but dinosaurs actually came in many shapes and sizes from the chicken sized Microraptor to the biggest dinosaur ever, the Argentinosaurus.

The word Dinosaur actually means "terrible lizard" in Greek. Not all reptiles then were considered dinosaurs. They had to walk upright on two legs like chickens or on four legs like elephants to be regarded as dinosaurs. The ones that walked flat on their belly like crocodiles or flew in the air like the Pterosaurs or swam in the ocean like the Plesiosaurs are not regarded as dinosaurs.

Dinosaurs are extinct today. In fact, they were extinct long before humans walked the Earth. But we still have their closest ancestors which some people call living dinosaurs: birds. Birds actually evolved from dinosaurs. So, the next time you eat a fried chicken, remember that you are actually chomping into the flesh of a cousin of the T-Rex.

Tyrannosaurus Rex or T-Rex is said to be one of the largest known meat-eating dinosaurs that ever lived. The word Tyrannosaurus means "tyrant lizard" in Greek and Rex means "king" in Latin, so the T-Rex is the king of the tyrant lizards. This dinosaur was a well-designed killing machine, with massive bone-crushing jaws and strong legs for running. It did have very tiny arms because they were unnecessary for this predator. The T-rex lived in the forests of North America during the Cretaceous period and became extinct when a massive asteroid hit the Earth about 65 million years ago.

Another dinosaur that looked a little like the T-Rex but with bigger arms is the Allosaurus, the name meaning "different lizard" in Greek. It was different because it had a weird shaped skull unlike the other dinosaurs.

If you have watched Jurassic Park then you know that the Velociraptor is the one dinosaur you need to be worried about the most. The name Velociraptor means "swift robber" in Greek and boy are they fast. They are also thought to be among the smartest dinosaurs. They lived around 75 million to 71 million years ago during the Cretaceous Era. They had a sharp sickle shaped claw on each foot like a rooster which they use to slice into their prey.

Stegosaurus was a large, plant eating dinosaur roughly the size of a bus that had two rows of bony plates along the entire top of its body and sharp horns on its tail. The word Stegosaurus means "roof lizard" in Greek because the plates look like roof tiles and when it was first discovered, Paleontologists thought that it lay flat on its back like a roof. The bony plates may have been used to soak up heat from sunlight, to keep it warm at night. It lived around 150 million to 155 million years ago during the Jurassic period. They were extinct long before T-rex existed.

Triceratops was another massive reptile about the size of an African elephant, with three horns, two big ones above its eyes and one small one on its snout. The word Triceratops means "three horn face" in Greek. These horns were most likely used in combat as well as a visual display for mating. Triceratops roamed North America alongside T-rex during the Cretaceous period and also died out during the asteroid collision.

Brontosaurus was a huge plant eating dinosaur with a very long neck and a very long tail that lived in the late Jurassic and early Cretaceous period, between 163 million to 100 million years ago. They probably existed alongside the Stegosaurus, Triceratops and T-rex. The word Brontosaurus means "thunder lizard" in Greek. Other long necked long tail dinosaurs include the biggest Argentinosaurus and the Seismosaurus.

Pterosaurs are reptiles with large skin wings. The name Pterosaur means "wing lizards" in Greek. These reptiles were around during the late Triassic Era to the end of the Cretaceous Era, between 228 million to 66 million years ago. The largest Pterosaurs are known as Pteranodons and had wingspans of more than 23 feet.

These dinosaurs were extinct long before humans walked the Earth, most of which died out in a mass extinction thought to be created by a massive asteroid collision off the Gulf of Mexico around 65 million years ago. Human were thought to have first appeared around 5 million to 7 million years ago.

10 LET'S LEARN CHEMISTRY

Chemistry is the study of matter and the chemical reactions between substances. It is the science of what things are made of and what are their properties. Matter is essentially anything in the universe that takes up space and has mass. Chemistry is involved in everything we do, from growing and cooking food to cleaning our homes and bodies to launching a space shuttle. Chemistry is one of the physical sciences that help us to describe and explain our world.

A Chemist is a person who studies Chemistry, or a scientist who works with chemicals or studies their reactions. In some parts of the world, a person who works or runs a drugstore or pharmacy is also known as a chemist, but this is a totally different job.

The Periodic Table of the Elements

Group→	1	2	3	4	5	6	7	8	9	10	11	12	13	14	15	16	17	18
Period 1	1 H																	2 He
2	3 Li	4 Be											5 B	6 C	7 N	8 O	9 F	10 Ne
3	11 Na	12 Mg											13 Al	14 Si	15 P	16 S	17 Cl	18 Ar
4	19 K	20 Ca	21 Sc	22 Ti	23 V	24 Cr	25 Mn	26 Fe	27 Co	28 Ni	29 Cu	30 Zn	31 Ga	32 Ge	33 As	34 Se	35 Br	36 Kr
5	37 Rb	38 Sr	39 Y	40 Zr	41 Nb	42 Mo	43 Tc	44 Ru	45 Rh	46 Pd	47 Ag	48 Cd	49 In	50 Sn	51 Sb	52 Te	53 I	54 Xe
6	55 Cs	56 Ba		72 Hf	73 Ta	74 W	75 Re	76 Os	77 Ir	78 Pt	79 Au	80 Hg	81 Tl	82 Pb	83 Bi	84 Po	85 At	86 Rn
7	87 Fr	88 Ra		104 Rf	105 Db	106 Sg	107 Bh	108 Hs	109 Mt	110 Ds	111 Rg	112 Cn	113 Nh	114 Fl	115 Mc	116 Lv	117 Ts	118 Og

Lanthanides	57 La	58 Ce	59 Pr	60 Nd	61 Pm	62 Sm	63 Eu	64 Gd	65 Tb	66 Dy	67 Ho	68 Er	69 Tm	70 Yb	71 Lu
Actinides	89 Ac	90 Th	91 Pa	92 U	93 Np	94 Pu	95 Am	96 Cm	97 Bk	98 Cf	99 Es	100 Fm	101 Md	102 No	103 Lr

Chemists use the Periodic Table to display all the known chemical elements, which are arranged according to their atomic numbers. In total there are 118 elements in the table starting with Hydrogen (1) and ending with Oganesson (118). The first 94 elements from Hydrogen to Plutonium (94) occur naturally while the rest are synthesized by humans. The atomic number for the element represents the number of protons that element has in its nucleus.

Noble gases are a group of chemical elements that display the following properties under standard conditions: gasses that are odorless, colorless, monatomic and very low chemical reactivity. There are seven noble gases, which are Helium, Neon, Argon, Krypton, Xenon, Radon and Oganesson.

Here are some of the chemical elements that you encountered in the jokes earlier along with their symbols and atomic number:
1) Hydrogen – H – 1
2) Helium – He – 2
3) Carbon – C – 6
4) Oxygen – O – 8
5) Sodium – Na – 11 (Na comes from Natrium, the Latin name for Sodium Carbonate)
6) Magnesium – Mg – 12
7) Argon – Ar – 18
8) Potassium – K – 19 (K comes from Kalium, the Latin name for alkali)
9) Iron – Fe – 26 (Fe comes from Ferum, the Latin name for Iron)
10) Cobalt – Co – 27
11) Zinc – Zn – 30
12) Bromine – Br – 35
13) Yttrium – Y – 39
14) Barium - Ba – 56
15) Radon – Rn – 86
16) Curium – Cm – 96

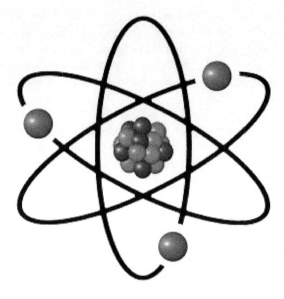

Every element is made up of an atom. An atom is the fundamental piece of matter. In simple terms, atoms are made up of a nucleus which contains protons and neutrons, and electrons that fly around the nucleus as a cloud. The number of protons it has in its nucleus is stated by its atomic number. Therefore, the element Oxygen has 8 protons. In a stable atom, this is also the number of neutrons and electrons that the atom has. Protons are positively charged, electrons are negatively charged and neutrons are neutral. When an atom loses or gains an electron, it is known as an ion.

When 2 or more atoms bond together, they form a molecule. This bond is known as a covalent bond, and it happens when atoms share electron pairs between them. We looked at a few molecules in the jokes. These include:

1)H_2O which is water. Can also be written as HOH.

2)H_2O_2 which is hydrogen peroxide, a poisonous substance

3)H_2SO_4 which is sulfuric acid, a very strong mineral acid

4)OK which is Oxygen and Potassium, but this is not a valid molecule, just part of the joke

5)NaBrO which is Sodium hypobromite

6)OMg which is Oxygen and Magnesium, also just a joke

7)CoRnY which is Cobalt, Radon and Yttrium, another joke

8)$NO_3(-)$ which is Nitrate, natural chemicals found in soil, air and water

Methylated spirits are poisonous alcohol solutions used as a solvent as well as fuel for burners and stoves.

Precipitation is the process of acquiring an insoluble solid by combining certain solutions. The solid is created from the chemical reaction of the two solutions.

An alloy is a combination of a metal with another metal or nonmetal. Examples of alloys are brass, bronze and steel.

Alkynes are unsaturated hydrocarbons used in many industries. Hydrocarbons are organic molecules that contain only Hydrogen and Carbon in various combinations. Benzene is an example of a hydrocarbon with the molecular formula $C6H6$ and is used in gasoline.

When two liquids are able to mix with each other they are said to be miscible. Alcohol is miscible with water, but oil is immiscible with water.

11 LET'S LEARN BIOLOGY

Biology is the study of life and living organisms, including their physical structure, chemical processes, molecular interactions, physiological mechanisms, development and evolution. Biology is a huge area of science with dozens of branches, but these can be grouped into three major branches: Zoology, Botany and Microbiology. Zoology studies animal, including those that are already extinct. Botany studies plants. Microbiology studies microscopic organisms.

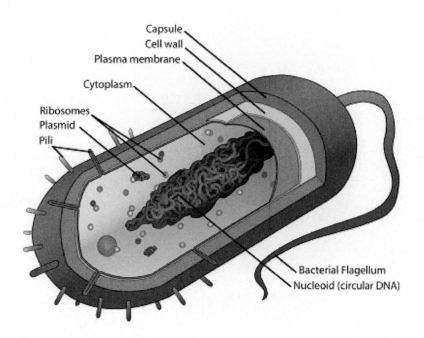

The basic structure in Biology for both plants and animals is the cell. The word cell comes from Latin meaning "small room" and is the smallest unit of life, containing biomolecules enclosed within a membrane that make up life. Our body contains trillions of different cells that perform a variety of function. These includes skin cells, blood cells and so much more.

The nucleus is a structure inside of a cell that stores DNA and coordinates the cell's activities.

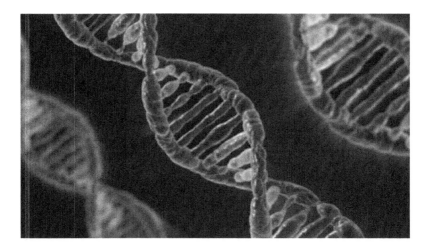

DNA stands for deoxyribonucleic acid and is a complex molecule that contains the genetic code of every organism. It is shaped like a double helix. The DNA stores the information of a person like an instruction manual of what the person should look like and how his body should function. This it does through a complex coding system that involves four chemical bases: Adenine (A), Guanine (G), Cytosine (C) and Thymine (T).

DNA is carried in thread like packages called chromosomes. Different organisms have a different number of chromosomes. Humans for example have 23 pairs, while cats have 19 pairs.

Cells replicate through a proses called mitosis in which a parent cell divides itself into two exact replicas, sharing its chromosomes between both the daughter cells.

When a male and a female mate, the genetic information from their DNA will combine to form a new organism that has some characteristics from both its parents. These are called genes. Genetics is the study of these genes.

A gene pool is a collection of all genes in a population. This can mean the collection of genes for frogs in a pond, trees in a forest or even people in a city.

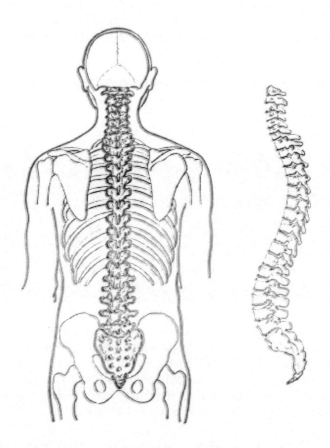

The spinal cord is a long and fragile tube that starts from the base of the brain and continues down to the bottom of the spine. It contains nerves that carry messages between the brain and the rest of the body. All vertebrates have spinal cords while invertebrates do not. The spinal cord is largely encased in the spinal column or backbone, which is a series of bones (31 segments for humans) that protects it. The dorsal horns on the spinal cord contain sensory neurons for senses while the ventral horns contain motor neurons for movement.

Veins are tubes in the blood circulation system of the body that carries oxygen depleted blood towards the heart. Drawings of the blood system usually depict veins as being blue, though this is just to differentiate them from arteries. Arteries carry oxygen rich blood away from the heart to transport to the entire body.

Germs are tiny microscopic organisms that include bacteria, viruses, protozoa and fungi. They can easily be passed from one person to another, through food and water and even through the air. Not all germs can harm you, though some can be very deadly.

A tardigrade, also known as a water bear, is one of the most amazing microscopic animals ever. This 8-legged creature is known as an extremophile, because it is a class of organisms that can survive the harshest conditions that other organisms cannot. It is said that tardigrades are the hardiest of all extremophiles. They can survive extreme temperatures, extreme pressure, air depravation, radiation, dehydration and starvation. In fact, tardigrades have been found frozen in a 2000-year-old ice sheet and were successfully brought back to life.

Microbiologists use microbial cultures as a method of multiplying microbes in Petri dishes, to reproduce them under controlled laboratory conditions.

Marine biologists study life in the oceans. They tag sea animals such as whales, dolphins and sharks to study them and to follow their migratory pattern. These tags are equipped with electronic and data sensors that tell the location of the animal as well as its data when it was tagged.

Frogs are a member of the Amphibian class. They may look like reptiles, but they are not. Amphibians do not have scales like reptiles and generally they lay their eggs in water because the eggs do not have hard shells. Toads are like frogs but have a few different characteristics. The easiest way to tell them apart is frogs have slimy skin while a toad's is dry and bumpy. Frogs and toads are carnivores and eat mainly insects. Medium sized frogs also eat worms and the large ones are even known to eat small snakes, mice and other small frogs.

The Bald Eagle is the proud national bird symbol of the United States of America. But it is definitely not bald, it has a head of gorgeous white feathers. The bald in its name comes from an old English word piebald which means "white headed". Bald Eagles live near large bodies of water since their favorite food is fish. Other than fish, they also catch rodents and small animals.

Tigers are mammals belonging to the feline or cat species. They are easily recognizable for their dark vertical stripes on an orange-brown fur, and white bellies. Tigers are apex predators, meaning that nothing hunts them for food. However, humans from certain countries do hunt them for their fur, teeth and supposed medicinal properties. Big cats with spots include leopards, jaguars and cheetahs and they can be differentiated by the type of spots they have, other than the size of their bodies.

Dogs have a much more sensitive hearing than humans. Almost all adult humans cannot hear sounds over 20,000 Hertz. Dogs however can hear as high as 65,000 Hertz. These sounds are too high pitch for us. Apart from frequency, dogs can also hear sounds that are too faint for us to hear.

Ivan Petrovich Pavlov was a Russian physiologist who is infamous for his experiments with dogs when he wanted to prove his theory in classical conditioning. In his experiments, Pavlov used a metronome as a trigger to illicit a response. Each time the metronome started clicking, the dogs would be given food and Pavlov would measure the dog's salivation. After a number of repeats of the procedure, Pavlov noted that the dogs would still salivate when they hear the metronome, even if no food is then presented. This is because the dogs had learned to associate the sound of the metronome to food. Later stories confused the trigger as a bell instead of a metronome.

Just like animals, plants also have male and female reproduction organs. But unlike animals, all plants have both on them, located inside a flower. The female reproduction organ is called the pistil and can be found down inside the flower, typically a swollen base that contains ovules or what will someday become seeds. The male reproduction organ is called the stamen and is tiny stalks that stick out of the flower. Stamens produce pollen. Pollen is a fine powder that combines with the ovules to form seeds. It is this that causes hay fever for people with allergies. The pollen gets transported from the stamen to an organ called a stigma, gets pulled down a tube called a style and finally reaches the ovule in the pistil. Insects like bees and butterflies help transport the pollen.

Mushrooms are not plants, they are fungi. The three major differences but between plants and fungi are their color, the way they obtain food and their method of reproduction. Plants are green because they contain chlorophyll for photosynthesis while mushrooms are not green. Photosynthesis is how plants obtain food from sunlight. Mushrooms obtain food from dead or decaying animals and other plants and can usually be found in damp places. Plants reproduce by making seeds, while mushrooms reproduce by producing spores.

12 LET'S LEARN PHYSICS

Physics is the study of matter and its motion through space and time, along with related concepts such as energy and force. Physicists study nature in an attempt to understand how the universe behaves.

Quantum Physics governs the way the universe behaves at atomic levels which is very different from the way larger objects behave. The concepts and theories of quantum physics can be pretty weird at times. Most of quantum physics is theoretical and only proven with mathematical equations but its theories have helped further other branches of physics. Among the weird theories of quantum physics is the Schrodinger's Cat thought experiment, which says that if a cat is placed in a sealed box with a vial of poison randomly timed to be released, we do not know that state the cat is in, whether it is dead or alive, until we open the box and observe it. Therefore, it is both dead and alive. This is in relation to a quantum theory that says that the state of a particle cannot be determined unless it is observed. Therefore, it exists as a probability of all states and collapses to form a singular state when observed.

One of the things that Quantum Physics is able to do is form working theories about the early seconds of the Universe after the Big Bang, when the universe was extremely hot and general physics did not apply.

Albert Einstein was a German born theoretical physicist who is best known for his Theory of Relativity. In General Relativity, Einstein's space-time theory explains what happens when an object travels near the speed of light as well as the motion of massive objects in the universe. Einstein's most famous equation is $E=mc2$, which means energy is equivalent to mass of matter multiplied by the speed of light squared.

Neils Bohr was a Danish physicist that proposed that electrons revolve around the nucleus of an atom in table orbits but can jump from one energy level to another either by releasing or gaining energy.

The fastest thing in the universe is light, travelling at 299,792,458 m/s. Nothing is said to be able to break this universal speed limit. A photon is a massless elementary particle and it is basic unit of light.

Visible light, also known as white light, actually consists of a collection of component colors. When light passes through a transparent prism, the white light is separated into its component colors in a process called dispersion. The colors that we can see are red, orange, yellow, green, blue and violet. This is because light of different color travel at different wave frequencies and when they travel through a medium denser than air, they will bend at varying degrees. We see the same effect when light travels through raindrops, what we call a rainbow.

Nuclear fission is the process where the nucleus of an atom splits into two or more smaller nuclei releasing energy in the process. Nuclear physicists commonly use large nuclei such as Uranium-235 in nuclear fission to harness nuclear energy. Uranium-238 occurs naturally in nature but is not as efficient in the harnessing of energy as Uranium-235 so is rarely used.

Quarks are elementary particles that combine to form composite particles called hadrons. Examples of hadrons include protons and neutrons.

Stable atoms have the same number of electrons as protons and neutrons. When an atom loses an electron, it becomes a positively charged ion. And when it gains an electron it becomes negatively charged.

In the physical world, matter is stated to exist in one of three states: solid, liquid or gas.

Electricity is the flow of an electric charge through a conductor.

The ohm, named after the physicist Georg Ohm, is defined as an electrical resistance between two points of a conductor. Ohm's Law states that the electrical current through a conductor between two points is directly proportional to the voltage across the two points.

The Kelvin Scale is a temperature scale used by scientist more than Celsius or Fahrenheit. This is for a number of reasons. Firstly, absolute zero, which is the coldest possible temperature is 0K (zero Kelvin) or -273.15 Celcius. By using the Kelvin Scale, scientists do not need to use negative numbers. Also, because a change in 1 degree Kelvin is also a change in 1 degree Celsius, it makes it easier to convert between the two scales. Water freezes at 273.15 Kelvin (0 degree Celsius) and boils at 373.15 Kelvin or 100 degrees Celsius. The scale was named in honor of the physicist Lord Kelvin.

Friction is the force between two surfaces that are sliding or trying to slide across each other. This force exerts itself opposite for the direction of moving thus either slowing down or stopping the movement.

Inertia is a force what keeps objects that at rest stationary and keeps objects that are moving at a constant velocity. Objects that are stagnant will only move and objects that are moving will either slow down or gain moment when provided with an outside force. This is also known as Newton's First Law.

13 LET'S LEARN ASTRONOMY

Astronomy is the scientific study of celestial objects such as stars, planets, comets, and galaxies and phenomena that originate outside the Earth's atmosphere such as the cosmic background radiation.

Nicolaus Copernicus was a famous Polish mathematician and astronomer who formulated the model of the universe where the sun was the center of the universe and the earth revolved around the sun with everything else. Before this, people believed that the Earth was the center of the universe and the sun, moon, planets and stars revolved around it. While he did give us a simple model of the solar system, we now know that the sun is not the center of the universe, in that it revolves along with other stars around the center of our galaxy.

An astronaut or cosmonaut is a person trained by a human spaceflight program to command, pilot, or serve as a crew member of a spacecraft. As of November 2018, the corps has 38 active astronauts and 18 "management astronauts", who are "employed at NASA but are no longer eligible for flight assignment". The highest number of active astronauts at one time, was in 2000 when there were 149.

On May 5, 1961, Alan B. Shepard made it into space and back just 23 days after Russian cosmonaut Yuri Gagarin became the first human to do so. Less than a year later, John Glenn became the first American to orbit the Earth.

On July 20, 1969, Neil Armstrong became the first human to step foot on the moon, followed by Buzz Aldrin about 3 hours later. Another astronaut who travelled with them, Michael Collins, stayed in orbit around the moon to perform experiments and take pictures. They travelled to the moon in the Apollo 11 spacecraft. In total there have been 12 astronauts who have walked on the moon.

Astronauts travel into space by being launched inside of a huge rocket.

An orbit is a repeating trajectory of an object around another object or space. Moons orbit around planets and planets orbit around the sun. While the orbit of the moon is more or less circular, the orbits of planets are actually an ellipse which is more of an oval than a circle.

A satellite is an object that orbits around a bigger object. There are two kinds of satellites: natural for example moons that orbit a planet and artificial such as the telecommunication satellites that we have launched into space.

The International Space Station is one of our most famous satellites after the Hubble Space Telescope. Launched in 1998, it was a collaboration between the space agencies of the US, Russia, Canada, Japan and the European Space Agency. It is large and in low orbit, if you know where to look you can probably spot it, looking like a fast-moving airplane. It orbits the Earth at 5 miles a second.

The Moon is an astronomical body orbiting Earth as its only natural satellite. It is the fifth-largest satellite in the Solar System, and by far the largest among planetary satellites relative to the size of the planet that it orbits.

Our moon is a lifeless object that is 384,400 km away from the Earth. It has no atmosphere and has a gravity that is much lower than Earth's, which is why astronauts look like they are hopping when moving around it.

An eclipse happens when one object in space moves in front of another object when viewed from Earth, obscuring the object behind it. A solar eclipse is when the moon's shadow crosses the Earth surface because the moon is between the Earth and the sun. A lunar eclipse is when the Earth shadow moves across the moon because the Earth is between the moon and the sun.

The moon is just a solid rock and does not give produce its own light. The moonlight that we see from Earth is actually the moon reflecting sunlight. The Lunar Phase is a sequence of phases based on the amount of sunlight reflected by the moon. It starts with a Full Moon the begins to take on a thinner crescent shape known as waning before becoming totally dark, known as a new moon. It then starts getting back its crescent shape known as waxing before becoming a full moon again.

A full moon occurs when Earth is located between the Sun and the Moon. The full moon occurs roughly once a month.

Planets are objects that orbit the sun and are large enough to have a gravity. We once believed that we had nine planets but after some heated debate, we now accept that we have 8, with Pluto being demoted to the status of dwarf planet. Dwarf planets are smaller sized planet-like objects that are mainly located near the Kuiper Belt on the outskirts of the solar system. There are 5 known dwarf planets: Pluto the biggest, Ceres, Haumea, Makemake and Eris. Ceres is the only dwarf planet located in the asteroid belt between Mars and Jupiter.

A Mars Rover is a small motor vehicle that travels across the surface of Mars collecting data and performing tasks. In total there has been 6 Mars rovers sent to the planet. The first two however failed, so only 4 have managed to work on the planet: Sojourner, Spirit, Opportunity, Curiosity. Out of these 4 only one is still operational today, known as Curiosity.

Earth is the only known planet in the entire universe to house life forms. While some scientists have hypothesized that they may be life on other planets in the universe, we have so far found no evidence of life outside of our planet.

The Sun or Sol is the star that lies at the center of our solar system, with the planets orbiting around it. It is 151.56 million kilometers from Earth. The light from the sun is so bright that it blocks out almost all other objects in space from being seen, except maybe the moon that sometimes appear in the daytime. One full orbit around the sun is known as a year, with different planets have different number of Earth days in a year. The Earth revolves around the sun a full circle in 365 days.

Our sun is ridiculously hot. Temperatures reach a melting 10 million degrees Fahrenheit at its surface and the center reaches 27 million degrees.

Telescopes allow us to see distance objects in more detail. Originally, telescopes were made by placing two lenses of different sizes on opposite ends of a tube, but these days we have telescopes that don't even have lenses. Radio telescopes for example are parabolic dishes that collect radio waves and reflect it into a receiver. The Hubble Space Telescope is a huge telescope that has been orbiting the Earth since 1990 and because the is no visual interference from the weather, has provided us some of the most detailed images of the universe.

A meteor is a space rock that enters the Earth's atmosphere. This is also known as a shooting star. Most meteors burn up due to atmospheric friction before it lands on the ground, but some do make it. A meteor shower happens when many meteors fall at the same time, usually due to the Earth passing into the remnants of a comet's tail.

A comet is an icy rock that also orbits the sun but generally in a very large very elliptical orbit that brings it out to the far outer borders of the solar system before circling back and moving very close to the sun. On its approach, the heat from the sun releases gas that was frozen on the comet, which it spews behind it giving it a tail. The most famous comet is the Hailey's Comet which flies by around the Earth's location every 75 years. The next time it can be seen will be in 2061.

A constellation is a group of stars that we can see that forms a pattern which people in ancient times thought represented animals, mythological beasts, heroes and gods. The twelve major constellations form the zodiac which we use in our horoscope.

A light-year is the distance light travels in one year. How far is that? Multiply the number of seconds in one year by the number of miles or kilometers that light travels in one second, and there you have it: one light-year. It's about 5.88 trillion miles (9.5 trillion km).

14 LET'S LEARN METEOROLOGY

Meteorology is the scientific study of the atmosphere that focuses on weather processes and forecasting.

A meteorologist is a specialized scientist who focuses on some aspect of the atmosphere, and who uses scientific principles to observe, understand and be able to explain or forecast how the earth's atmosphere affects the earth and everyone on it.

A weatherman or weather forecaster is a person who forecasts and reports the weather. They are generally not meteorologists; they just report the weather.

If you want to know what the weather will be like within the next week, a weather forecast can give you a really good idea of what to expect. A seven-day forecast can accurately predict the weather about 80 percent of the time and a five-day forecast can accurately predict the weather approximately 90 percent of the time.

In Mexico, there are two main seasons. Although there is some variation in temperature over the year, the most obvious difference is between rainy and dry seasons. The rainy season through most of Mexico falls roughly from May through September or October. During the rest of the year, there is little or no rain.

Rain in England is really not that much, it's about the same as New York or Miami. But because it is an island surround by the ocean on all sides, the country does experience its fair share of rain all over making it seem like it rains almost every day.

A tornado is a violent rotating column of air extending from a thunderstorm to the ground. The most violent tornadoes are capable of tremendous destruction with wind speeds of up to 300 mph. They can destroy large buildings, uproot trees and hurl vehicles hundreds of yards. The term "twister" is just slang for "tornado" because of how it acts; technically, a tornado is a rapidly twisting vortex that most of the time gains strength as it moves along land. "Tornado" is generally the term used by meteorologists.

A hurricane is a large rotating storm with high speed winds that forms over warm waters in tropical areas. Hurricanes have sustained winds of at least 74 miles per hour and an area of low air pressure in the center called the eye. The scientific name for a hurricane is a tropical cyclone. There is one part of a hurricane where things are quite different, though. It is called the eye, and it usually exists in the center of a hurricane. The eye can vary greatly in terms of both shape and size. The eye of a hurricane is often circular or oval in shape. This may be why it is called an eye, since it's shaped somewhat like a human eye. A hurricane's eye can be as small as only a couple of miles wide. Most hurricane eyes, however, range in size from 20 miles wide to more than 60 miles wide. Unlike the raging winds that exist throughout the remainder of a hurricane, inside the eye it is mostly calm. The peaceful, light winds within the eye contrast severely with the winds that make up the edges of the eye, known as the eyewall. The winds in the eyewall are usually the most severe and destructive winds in the entire hurricane.

A cold front is defined as the transition zone where a cold air mass is replacing a warmer air mass. Cold fronts generally move from northwest to southeast. The air behind a cold front is noticeably colder and drier than the air ahead of it. Commonly, when the cold front is passing, winds become gusty; there is a sudden drop in temperature, and heavy rain, sometimes with hail, thunder, and lightning. Lifted warm air ahead of the front produces cumulus or cumulonimbus clouds and thunderstorms.

An isobar is a line on a map that shows a meteorologist what the pressure is at the surface of the earth. They are lines that connect equal points of pressure. Isobars can be used to map atmospheric or air pressure in a way that makes it easier to understand. They can be used to find areas of low or high pressure over a broad area (like the U.S.), and they can tell us how intense the system may be.

A cloud is a visible accumulation of minute droplets of water, ice crystals, or both, suspended in the air. Though they vary in shape and size, all clouds are basically formed in the same way through the vertical of air above the condensation level. Clouds may also form in contact with the ground surface, too. The different types of clouds are cumulus, cirrus, stratus and nimbus. Clouds are not containers of water so that it goes empty after it rains. When the saturation point of cloud is reached, that is by the amount of water vapor it can hold, it condenses to form water droplets which precipitates as rains. Once all the water present in the clouds are precipitated then there will be no clouds!

Lighter, positively charged particles form at the top of clouds. Heavier, negatively charged particles sink to the bottom of the cloud. When the positive and negative charges grow large enough, a giant spark - lightning - occurs between the two charges within the cloud. Lightning can be either connect from one cloud to another or shoot from a cloud down to the ground. Lighting also has different appearances and is always accompanied by thunder. Types of cloud-to-ground lightning include staccato, forked, ribbon, and bead lightening.

The lightning conductor or rod is a metal rod or conductor mounted on top of a building and electrically connected to the ground through a thick wire, to protect the building in the event of lightning. Thick wires or stripes of copper or aluminum are used to conduct the lightning harmlessly to the ground.

15 LET'S LEARN GEOGRAPHY AND GEOLOGY

Geography is the study of places and the relationships between people and their environments. Geographers explore both the physical properties of Earth's surface and the human societies spread across it.

Geology is the study of the Earth, how it works and its 4.5 billion-year history. Geologists study some of society's most important problems, such as energy, water, and mineral resources; the environment; climate change; and natural hazards like landslides, volcanoes, earthquakes, and floods.

Egypt, country located in the northeastern corner of Africa. Egypt's heartland, the Nile River valley and delta, was the home of one of the principal civilizations of the ancient Middle East and, like Mesopotamia farther east, was the site of one of the world's earliest urban and literate societies. Pharaonic Egypt thrived for some 3,000 years through a series of native dynasties that were interspersed with brief periods of foreign rule.

The Great Sphinx of Giza, commonly referred to as the Sphinx of Giza or just the Sphinx, is a limestone statue of a reclining sphinx, a mythical creature with the body of a lion and the head of a human. Facing directly from West to East, it stands on the Giza Plateau on the west bank of the Nile in Giza, Egypt. The face of the Sphinx is generally believed to represent the pharaoh Khafre.

Russia, country that stretches over a vast expanse of eastern Europe and northern Asia. Once the preeminent republic of the Union of Soviet Socialist Republics (U.S.S.R.; commonly known as the Soviet Union), Russia became an independent country after the dissolution of the Soviet Union in December 1991. By far the world's largest country, it covers nearly twice the territory of Canada, the second largest. It extends across the whole of northern Asia and the eastern third of Europe, spanning 11 time zones and incorporating a great range of environments and landforms, from deserts to semiarid steppes to deep forests and Arctic tundra. Russia contains Europe's longest river, the Volga, and its largest lake, Ladoga. Russia also is home to the world's deepest lake, Baikal, and the country recorded the world's lowest temperature outside the North and South poles.

Crude oil is a naturally occurring, unrefined petroleum product composed of hydrocarbon deposits and other organic materials. A type of fossil fuel, crude oil can be refined to produce usable products such as gasoline, diesel, and various other forms of petrochemicals. Crude oil is the base for lots of products. These include transportation fuels such as gasoline, diesel, and jet fuel. They also include fuel oils used for heating and electricity generation.

A mountain is a large landform that rises above the surrounding land in a limited area, usually in the form of a peak. A mountain is generally considered to be steeper than a hill. Mountains are formed through tectonic forces or volcanism. These forces can locally raise the surface of the earth. Mountains are often thought of as being a hill which is larger than 600 meters (about 2,000 feet).

A volcano is a rupture in the crust of a planetary-mass object, such as Earth, that allows hot lava, volcanic ash, and gases to escape from a magma chamber below the surface. Earth's volcanoes occur because its crust is broken into 17 major, rigid tectonic plates that float on a hotter, softer layer in its mantle. Volcanoes happen when magma rises to the surface of the earth, which causes bubbles of gas to appear in it. This gas can cause pressure to build up in the mountain, and it eventually explodes. When the magma bursts out of the earth, it is called lava.

Sedimentary rocks are types of rock that are formed by the accumulation or deposition of small particles and subsequent cementation of mineral or organic particles on the floor of oceans or other bodies of water at the Earth's surface. Common sedimentary rocks include sandstone, limestone, and shale. These rocks often start as sediments carried in rivers and deposited in lakes and oceans. When buried, the sediments lose water and become cemented to form rock.

The definition of "granite" varies. A geologist might define granite as a coarse-grained, quartz- and feldspar-bearing igneous rock that is made up entirely of crystals. However, in the dimension stone trade, the word "granite" is used for any feldspar-bearing rock with interlocking crystals that are large enough to be seen with the unaided eye. By this classification, rocks such as anorthosite, gneiss, granite, granodiorite, diabase, monzonite, syenite, gabbro and others are all sold under the trade name of "granite." People have used granite for thousands of years. It is used as a construction material, a dimension stone, an architectural stone, a decorative stone, and it has also been used to manufacture a wide variety of products. Granite is used in buildings, bridges, paving, monuments, and many other exterior projects. Indoors, polished granite slabs and tiles are used in countertops, tile floors, stair treads and many other design elements. Granite is a prestige material, used in projects to produce impressions of elegance and quality.

In essence, igneous rocks are formed through the cooling and solidification of magma (or lava). As hot, molten rock rises to the surface, it undergoes changes in temperature and pressure that cause it to cool, solidify, and crystallize.

A quarry is a type of mine called an open pit mine, because it is open to the Earth's surface. Another type of mine, a sub-surface mine, consists of underground tunnels or shafts. The most common purpose of quarries is to extract stone for building materials. Quarries have been used for thousands of years.

Tectonic plates are pieces of Earth's crust and uppermost mantle, together referred to as the lithosphere. The plates are around 100 km thick and consist of two principal types of material: oceanic crust (also called sima from silicon and magnesium) and continental crust (sial from silicon and aluminium). From the deepest ocean trench to the tallest mountain, plate tectonics explains the features and movement of Earth's surface in the present and the past. Plate tectonics is the theory that Earth's outer shell is divided into several plates that glide over the mantle, the rocky inner layer above the core.

Gneiss is a high-grade metamorphic rock, meaning that it has been subjected to higher temperatures and pressures than schist. It is formed by the metamorphosis of granite, or sedimentary rock. Gneiss displays distinct foliation, representing alternating layers composed of different minerals. In simplified terms, you can think of gneiss as a metamorphic version of granite. Both gneiss and granite are made of feldspars, quartz, mica, and smaller amounts of dark colored minerals like hornblende. ... The difference between granite and gneiss is in their overall texture and movement. Granite is evenly speckled. Metamorphic Gneiss has many uses as a building material such as flooring, ornamental stones, gravestones, facing stones on buildings and work surfaces.

Fluorite is a very popular mineral, and it naturally occurs in all colors of the spectrum. It is one of the most varied colored minerals in the mineral kingdom, and the colors may be very intense and almost electric. Pure Fluorite is colorless; the color variations are caused by various impurities. Some colors are deeply colored, and are especially pretty in large well-formed crystals, which Fluorite often forms. Sometimes coloring is caused by hydrocarbons, which can be removed from a specimen by heating. Some dealers may apply oil treatment upon amateur Fluorite specimens to enhance luster.

16 LET'S LEARN MATHEMATICS

Mathematics is the study of numbers, shapes and patterns. The word comes from the Greek word "mathema" meaning "science, knowledge, or learning", and is sometimes shortened to maths. Mathematics includes the study of such topics as quantity (number theory), structure (algebra), space (geometry), and change (mathematical analysis).

The Möbius strip, also called the twisted cylinder, is a one-sided surface with no boundaries. It looks like an infinite loop. Like a normal loop, an ant crawling along it would never reach an end, but in a normal loop, an ant could only crawl along either the top or the bottom. A Möbius strip has only one side, so an ant crawling along it would wind along both the bottom and the top in a single stretch. A Möbius strip can be constructed by taking a strip of paper, giving it a half twist, then joining the ends together. Giant Möbius strips have been used as conveyor belts that last longer because the entire surface area of the belt gets the same amount of wear, and as continuous loop recording tapes to double the playing time.

A 90-degree angle is also known as a right angle. In geometry and trigonometry, a right angle is an angle of exactly 90°, corresponding to a quarter turn. The term is a calque of Latin angulus rectus; here rectus means "upright", referring to the vertical perpendicular to a horizontal base line.

Pi is the ratio of a circle's circumference to its diameter. So, for any circle, dividing its circumference by its diameter will give you the exact same number: 3.14159 or pi. Pi is also an irrational number, which means that its value cannot be expressed exactly as a simple fraction.

In mathematics and digital electronics, a binary number is a number expressed in the base-2 numeral system or binary numeral system, which uses only two symbols: typically "0" (zero) and "1" (one). The base-2 numeral system is a positional notation with a radix of 2.

Roman numerals are a number system developed in ancient Rome where letters represent numbers. The modern use of Roman numerals involves the letters I, V, X, L, C, D, and M, which is 1, 5, 10, 50, 500 and 1000.

The mean is the average of the numbers. It is easy to calculate: add up all the numbers, then divide by how many numbers there are. In other words, it is the sum divided by the count.

ABOUT THE AUTHOR

TIM KESSLER is a German born in Malaysia, speaks English, married to an Indian, drives a Japanese car and is half the time confused about all this. The rest of the time he loves traveling around the world and enjoying life to the fullest. Almost never taking life seriously except while queuing to buy a lottery ticket, he has always viewed the world with rose colored glasses.

From his travels, he has gathered a library's worth of stories, jokes and experiences which he now puts down on paper. His only desire in his writing is so that everyone who reads his work sees the world for the paradise it truly is.

Printed in Great Britain
by Amazon